This
Treasure Cove Story
belongs to

_____

SEVEN DWARFS FIND A HOUSE

A CENTUM BOOK 978-1-913265-99-1
Published in Great Britain by Centum Books Ltd.
This edition published 2020.

1 3 5 7 9 10 8 6 4 2

© 2020, 2019, 1952, 1948 by Disney Enterprises, Inc.
All Rights Reserved.

Centum Books Ltd, 20 Devon Square, Newton Abbot,
Devon, TQ12 2HR, UK.

www.centumbooksltd.co.uk | books@centumbooksltd.co.uk
CENTUM BOOKS Limited Reg. No. 07641486.

A CIP catalogue record for this book is available
from the British Library.

Printed in China.

centum

A Treasure Cove Story

Walt Disney's
Seven Dwarfs
FIND A HOUSE

By Annie North Bedford
Pictures by the Walt Disney Studio
Adapted by Julius Svendsen

Once upon a time, there were seven little men. They worked in a mine all day.

At night, they slept in hollow trees or in rocky caves or in nests of leaves. They had no place to call home.

Now, these little men were the best of
friends. They were Doc and Grumpy and
Happy and Bashful and Sneezy and Sleepy
— and Dopey, who never tried to talk.
They were the Seven Dwarfs.

One day, the Dwarfs decided that they must have a home. They asked their animal friends to help them. The animals soon found a house that would be just right.

Off through the woods marched the
seven little men, singing a merry 'Hi, hi-ho!'
as the animals led them along to the little
empty house.

Doc led the way in. They liked it fine.

And they started to clean. Sneezy went 'Katchoo!'

Sleepy didn't care much for work. He
headed for the little beds – seven in a row.
When Doc came hunting for him, Sleepy
was deep in his dreams.

'Wash time!' said Doc. All the Dwarfs were surprised. They had never bothered with soap and water and such.

But Doc said, 'No supper till your hands and faces are clean.'

So they washed in spite of themselves.

Soon Happy was busy fixing supper.

Bashful helped with the stirring.

Then supper was ready for the seven
little men – a delicious supper, too!

After supper, Grumpy sat and scowled
for a while.

But the others wanted to celebrate.
'Play for us, Grumpy,' they begged.
Grumpy scowled some more. He liked
to be teased. At last he sat down at the
organ to play.

Happy and Sleepy joined in and
what a lively time they had, playing
and singing and dancing long past
bedtime that night.

Then finally they all marched
off to bed – in their very own
house in the woods.

Treasure Cove Stories

Please contact Centum Books to receive the full list of titles in the *Treasure Cove Stories* series.
books@centumbooksltd.co.uk

Classic favourites

1 Three Little Pigs
2 Snow White and the Seven Dwarfs
3 The Fox and the Hound
- Hide-and-Seek
4 Dumbo
5 Cinderella
6 Cinderella's Friends
7 Alice in Wonderland
8 Mad Hatter's Tea Party from Alice in Wonderland
9 Mickey Mouse and his Spaceship
10 Peter Pan
11 Pinocchio
12 Mickey and the Beanstalk
13 Sleeping Beauty and the Good Fairies
14 The Lucky Puppy
15 Chicken Little
16 The Incredibles
17 Coco
18 Winnie the Pooh and Tigger
19 The Sword in the Stone
20 Mary Poppins
21 The Jungle Book
22 The Aristocats
23 Lady and the Tramp
24 Bambi
25 Bambi - Friends of the Forest

Recently published

50 Frozen
51 Cinderella is my Babysitter
52 Beauty and the Beast
- I am the Beast
53 Blaze and the Monster Machines
- Mighty Monster Machines
54 Blaze and the Monster Machines
- Dino Parade!
55 Teenage Mutant Ninja Turtles
- Follow the Ninja!

56 I am a Princess
57 The Big Book of Paw Patrol
58 Paw Patrol
- Adventures with Grandpa!
59 Paw Patrol - Pirate Pups!
60 Trolls
61 Trolls Holiday
62 The Secret Life of Pets
63 Zootropolis
64 Ariel is my Babysitter
65 Tiana is my Babysitter
66 Belle is my Babysitter
67 Paw Patrol
- Itty-Bitty Kitty Rescue
68 Moana
69 Nella the Princess Knight
 - My Heart is Bright!
70 Guardians of the Galaxy
71 Captain America
- High-Stakes Heist!
72 Ant-Man
73 The Mighty Avengers
74 The Mighty Avengers
- Lights Out!
75 The Incredible Hulk
76 Shimmer & Shine
- Wish Upon a Sleepover
77 Shimmer & Shine - Backyard Ballet
78 Paw Patrol - All-Star Pups!
79 Teenage Mutant Ninja Turtles
- Really Spaced Out!
80 I am Ariel
81 Madagascar
82 Jasmine is my Babysitter
83 How to Train your Dragon
84 Shrek
85 Puss in Boots
86 Kung Fu Panda
87 Beauty and the Beast - I am Belle
88 The Lion Guard
- The Imaginary Okapi
89 Thor - Thunder Strike!
90 Guardians of the Galaxy
- Rocket to the Rescue!
91 Nella the Princess Knight
- Nella and the Dragon
92 Shimmer & Shine
- Treasure Twins!

93 Olaf's Frozen Adventure
94 Black Panther
95 Trolls
- Branch's Bunker Birthday
96 Trolls - Poppy's Party
97 The Ugly Duckling
98 Cars - Look Out for Mater!
99 101 Dalmatians
100 The Sorcerer's Apprentice
101 Tangled
102 Avengers
- The Threat of Thanos
103 Puppy Dog Pals
- Don't Rain on my Pug-Rade
104 Jurassic Park
105 The Mighty Thor
106 Doctor Strange

Latest publications

107 Captain Marvel
108 The Invincible Iron Man
109 Black Panther
- Warriors of Wakanda
110 The Big Freeze
111 Ratatouille
112 Aladdin
113 Aladdin - I am the Genie
114 Seven Dwarfs Find a House
115 Toy Story
116 Toy Story 4
117 Paw Patrol - Jurassic Bark!
118 Paw Patrol
- Mighty Pup Power!
119 Shimmer & Shine
- Pet Talent Show!
120 SpongeBob SquarePants
- Krabby Patty Caper
121 The Lion King - I am Simba
122 Winnie the Pooh
- The Honey Tree
123 Frozen II
124 Baby Shark and the Colours of the Ocean
125 Baby Shark and the Police Sharks!
126 Trolls World Tour

*Book list may be subject to change.